SpOT hOLDS A BEAUTY COMPETITION

LITOR PUBLISHERS LTD – LONDON

Printed in Great Britain by A. Wheaton & Co.

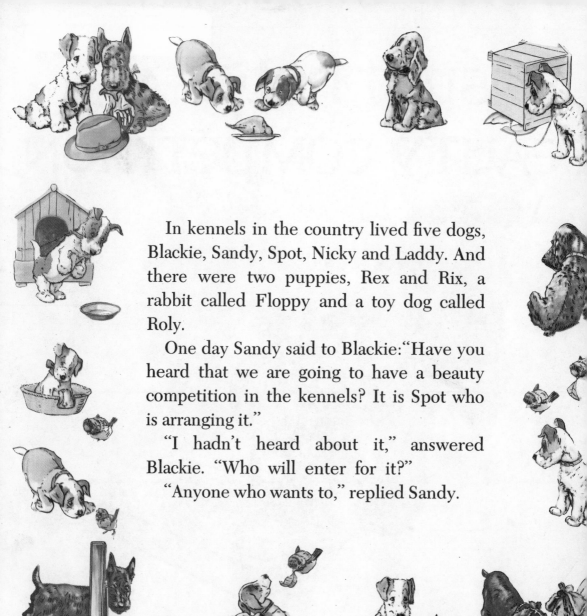

In kennels in the country lived five dogs, Blackie, Sandy, Spot, Nicky and Laddy. And there were two puppies, Rex and Rix, a rabbit called Floppy and a toy dog called Roly.

One day Sandy said to Blackie:"Have you heard that we are going to have a beauty competition in the kennels? It is Spot who is arranging it."

"I hadn't heard about it," answered Blackie. "Who will enter for it?"

"Anyone who wants to," replied Sandy.

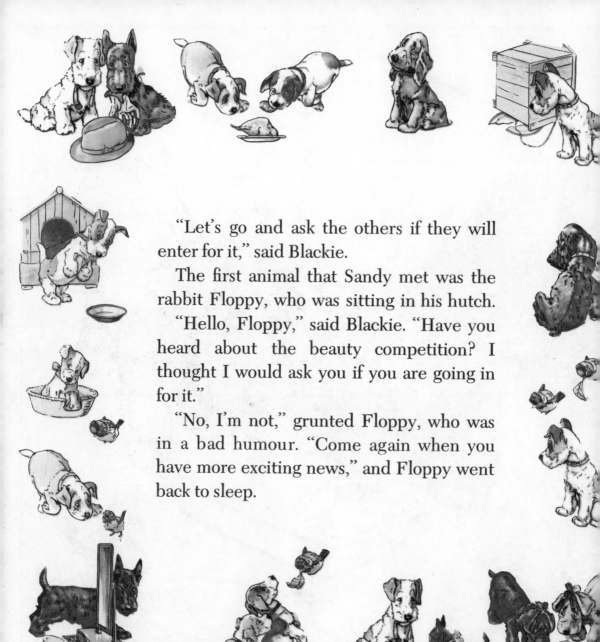

"Let's go and ask the others if they will enter for it," said Blackie.

The first animal that Sandy met was the rabbit Floppy, who was sitting in his hutch.

"Hello, Floppy," said Blackie. "Have you heard about the beauty competition? I thought I would ask you if you are going in for it."

"No, I'm not," grunted Floppy, who was in a bad humour. "Come again when you have more exciting news," and Floppy went back to sleep.

Meanwhile Blackie was asking Spot about the beauty competition.

Spot was the house-dog and he lay in a basket which stood on a fine warm rug.

"I have heard that you are arranging a beauty competition," said Blackie.

"Yes," answered Spot. "Of course my friend Laddy will be certain to get first prize."

"Oh? Really?" said Blackie. "Do you mean that no one else has a chance, then?"

"Oh well, there will be consolation prizes," promised Spot. "Fine prizes, too."

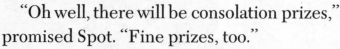

Laddy was in the bedroom, as usual, grooming himself ready for the competition.

He had jumped up on the dressing-table where there was powder, a hair brush and a mirror. And there he sat most of the day. He preened himself in front of the mirror and said to himself: "Just look! That is how a dog should look! Black, glossy hair, short beautiful legs and short ears, which stand straight up. I am bound to win!"

Spot was busy all the time arranging the competition. He needed labels: "First Prize" and "Second Prize" but it so happened that Spot was not very good at counting so he wrote "First Prize" on one label and "Third Prize" on the other.

At the last minute Spot decided that Laddy ought to enter for the competition wearing a hat and gloves, so he borrowed his Master's best blue hat and his yellow pigskin gloves.

Sandy and Blackie went into the dining room one day to ask the puppies Rex and Rix if they were going in for the competition. But Rex and Rix had hardly time to listen. They were busy stealing a whole roast goose.

Rex and Rix tugged on the table cloth until the dish and the goose landed on the floor.

"Prizes are all very well," said Rex, "but we have got a whole roast goose to ourselves!"

And out they trotted into the garden with it.

Blackie and Sandy went into the garden, too. The goose smelled so wonderful they just had to follow!

Rex and Rix chewed and munched and crunched and soon there were only the legs left.

"We will bury them here," said Rex, "just by the lawn." And both puppies began to dig a big hole.

WHOOSH! SLOSH! Earth and plants flew in the air and it wasn't long before the rest of the goose was buried and the hole filled in again.

"So that's that," barked Rix.

At last the day for the beauty competition arrived. Laddy was having a last brushing and combing when another dog trotted into the garden. She was a fox terrier called Foxie, and had come to enter the competition.

Now, have you guessed who won the first prize? Yes, it was Foxie, and Laddy only got a consolation prize. It wasn't so funny but that's just what happens when you feel sure of something.

But the one who came off worst was Spot. When his Master got to know who had taken his blue hat and pigskin gloves and given them to Laddy, Spot's Master became so angry he banished Spot from the house.

One day when Spot was lying in front of his kennel, a toy dog called Roly came up to him. Roly said for a joke:

"Shall we arrange a beauty competition? I am a Scottish terrier and have the right kind of looks to win!"

Spot was so angry he stood up on his back legs and took a big jump at Roly, who was quick to roll away on his wheels.

Poor Spot! He pulled over his kennel and broke his dish and his Master was angry again. But he didn't stay angry for long and soon Spot was back indoors and everyone was the best of friends once more.